GW00854852

Other cartoon giftbooks in this series:
The Fanatic's Guide to Cats   The Fanatic's Guide to Husbands
The Fanatic's Guide to Computers   The Fanatic's Guide to Love
The Fanatic's Guide to Dads   The Fanatic's Guide to D.I.Y.
The Fanatic's Guide to Golf   The Fanatic's Guide to Sex
The Wrinklies Guide to Staying Young at Heart

This hardback edition published simultaneously in 1998 by
Exley Publications Ltd. in Great Britain, and
Exley Publications LLC in the USA.

12   11   10   9   8   7   6   5   4   3   2   1

Copyright © Roland Fiddy, 1998

ISBN 1-86187-078-7

Printed in Hungary.

Exley Publications Ltd, 16 Chalk Hill, Watford, Herts, WD1 4BN, United Kingdom.
Exley Publications LLC, 232 Madison Avenue, Suite 1206, NY 10016, USA.

THE
Mobile
phone
CARTOON
BOOK

CARTOONS BY
ROLAND FIDDY

EXLEY
NEW YORK • WATFORD, UK

BEEP
BEEP

The Introvert

③